HERO

THE SLIPPERY SCHEMES OF
SUSHI MAN

STEVE BARLOW - STEVE SKIDMORE
ILLUSTRATED BY PIPI SPOSITO

Franklin Watts
First published in Great Britain in 2020
by The Watts Publishing Group

Text © Steve Barlow and Steve Skidmore 2020
Illustrations © Franklin Watts 2020
Design: Cathryn Gilbert

ISBN 978 1 4451 6947 7
ebook ISBN 978 1 4451 6949 1
Library ebook ISBN 978 1 4451 6948 4

1 3 5 7 9 10 8 6 4 2

Printed in Great Britain

Franklin Watts
An imprint of
Hachette Children's Group
Part of The Watts Publishing Group
Carmelite House
50 Victoria Embankment
London EC4Y 0DZ

An Hachette UK Company
www.hachette.co.uk

www.franklinwatts.co.uk

HOW TO BE A MEGAHERO

Some superheroes can read books with their X-ray vision without opening the covers or even when they're in a different room ...

Others can read them while flying through the air or stopping a runaway train.

But that stuff *IS* just small potatoes to you, because you're not a superhero. You're a *MEGAHERO*!

YES, this book is about **YOU**! And you don't just read it to the end and then stop. You read a bit: then you make a choice that takes you to a different part of the book. You might jump from Section 3 to 47 or 28!

If you make a good choice, *GREAT!*

BUUUUUUT ...

If you make the wrong choice ... *DA-DA-DAAAH!* **ALL KINDS OF BAD STUFF WILL HAPPEN.**

Too bad! It's no good turning green and tearing your shirt off. You'll just have to start again. But that won't happen, will it?

Because you're not a zero, or even a superhero. You are ... *MEGAHERO*!

You are a **BRILLIANT INVENTOR** — but one day **THE SUPER PARTICLE-ACCELERATING COSMIC RAY COLLIDER** you'd made out of old drinks cans, lawnmower parts and a mini black hole went critical and scrambled your molecules (nasty!). When you finally stopped screaming, smoking and bouncing off the walls, you found your body had changed! Now you can transform into any person, creature or object. **HOW AWESOME IS THAT?!!!**

You communicate with your **MEGACOMPUTER** companion, **PAL**, through your **MEGASHADES** sunglasses (which make you look pretty COOL, too). **PAL** controls the things you turn into and *almost hardly ever crashes and has to be turned off and on again!* This works perfectly — unless you have a bad WIFI signal, or **PAL** gets something wrong — but hey! That's computers for you, right?

Like all heroes, your job is to SAVE THE WORLD from **BADDIES AND THEIR EVIL SCHEMES**. But be back in time for supper. Even **MEGAHEROES** have to eat ...

Go to 1.

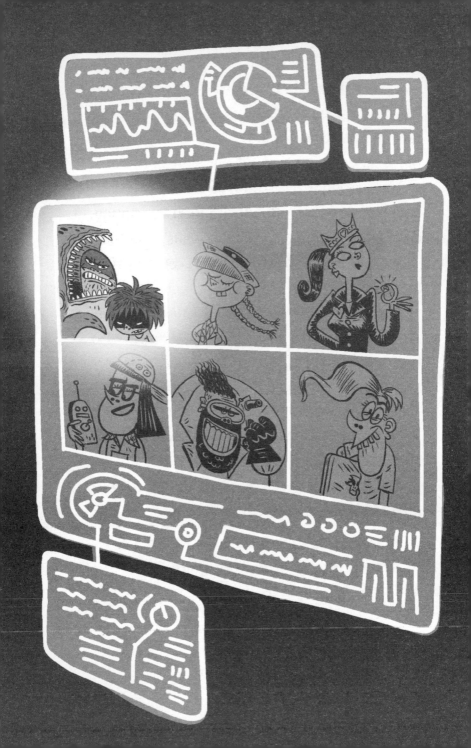

You are at your holiday home in the Bahamas, swimming with dolphins — which is even more fun when you can turn into a dolphin yourself!

The earphones in your *MEGASHADES* start beeping, and the **Augmented Reality** screens in the lenses flash.

Your *MEGACOMPUTER*, PAL, has an urgent message.

"I'M GETTING REPORTS OF A CRIME WAVE IN JAPAN."

"No problemo," you say. "I'm always ready to kick supervillain butt."

"THE ROBBERS AREN'T SUPERVILLAINS," says PAL. "THEY'RE ORDINARY PEOPLE. OFFICE WORKERS AND SHOP ASSISTANTS ARE ROBBING BANKS AND HOLDING UP SECURITY VANS."

"That is strange," you say. "Time to use my *MEGAMORPH* powers!"

To fly to Japan in bird form, go to 12.
To turn into a jet fighter, go to 28.

2

"Change me into something small and sneaky," you tell PAL.

Instantly you turn into a rat. "Good choice," you tell PAL.

You get out of the fish hold without being seen. Where should you go next?

To look under the decks at the bottom of the boat, go to 14.

To find the captain's cabin, go to 30.

To find the crew quarters, go to 23.

3

You call an ambulance for Mr Fugumoto, then check in with PAL.

"IF **SUSHI MAN** IS USING THE POISON OF THE **FUGU**," says PAL, "HE MUST HAVE A WELL-EQUIPPED LAB."

But how do you find **SUSHI MAN**'s lab?

To investigate a WHOOSHI SUSHI restaurant kitchen, go to 21.

To find out where the restaurant's food comes from, go to 38.

4

PAL turns you into an octopus. Using your tentacles, you open the box and slither away to do some exploring.

You seem to be in a fish processing factory. All around you are machines and fridges and one heavy steel door guarded by two huge sumo wrestlers.

To turn into a wrestling champ, go to 34.
To turn into a fierce bear, go to 19.

5

You leap forward and suddenly disappear.
SUSHI MAN stops in mid-gesture and stares around.

"Hey! Where did you go?"

"I'm still here." Your voice is muffled. "I turned into the germ of a nasty tummy bug and flew straight into your mouth. Now, I'm in your gut. I think it's time you had a taste of your own medicine!"

SUSHI MAN collapses, holding his belly and groaning with pain.

Go to 50.

5

6

You land. "Make me **SCARY**," you tell PAL.

Instantly you turn into a tiny spider.

"A spider?" you say. "What's scary about a very small spider?"

"WELL, ALL SPIDERS SCARE ME!" says PAL. "TOO MANY LEGS!"

To stay in spider form, go to 33.

To turn back into *MEGAHERO*, go to 17.

7

"Turn me into something faster than this shark," you tell PAL.

You turn into a penguin.

"What's wrong with a speedboat?" you cry.

"STOP MOANING," says PAL. "THE SHARK WON'T CATCH YOU NOW."

PAL is right. You zoom away. But then you realise something else is on your tail — it's a killer whale, which can swim as fast as you can. You see a fishing net ahead.

To swim into the net, go to 31.

To try to escape the net, go to 18.

8

As soon as you arrive on deck and change to human form, you hear crew members approaching. Time for another change.

To turn back into a pufferfish, go to 32.

To turn into something slim and stealthy, go to 15.

9

You turn into a clipboard. You realise you have made a good choice when a scientist picks you up from the top of the pile. The scan lets him through the door into **SUSHI MAN**'s secret lab!

To the scientist's amazement, his clipboard rears up and bangs him on the head, knocking him out. You change back into human form.

A mocking voice behind you drawls, "**MEGAHERO**! I'm glad you could make it!"

You turn. "**Wasabi Boy**?"

"Good guess." **Wasabi Boy** gestures to the squad of sumo wrestlers at his heels. "Get him!"

You need to be able to take on the heavies!

To turn into a rhinoceros, go to 20.

To turn into a bulldozer, turn to 27.

Arriving at **WHOOSHI SUSHI HQ,** you go inside and ask to see the owner of the restaurant chain, Mr Fugumoto. "I'm here on official business," you say.

Moments later, a door opens and half a dozen big men wearing black suits appear. With them is an older man in a grey suit.

"I am Mr Fugumoto," he says. "And **YOU** are in big trouble."

His men close in around you, menacingly.

To turn into something quick to get away, go to 44.

To turn into something strong to fight them off, go to 36.

11

PAL turns you into an ice cube. You lie around and chill as your box is loaded onto a van. After a short journey, it is taken out again.

To turn into an octopus, go to 4.

To stay as an ice cube, go to 43.

To turn into a salmon, go to 26.

12

"Turn me into a bird," you tell PAL.

"EVEN THE FASTEST BIRD WOULD TAKE DAYS TO FLY FROM HERE TO JAPAN," says PAL. "IT'S ON THE OTHER SIDE OF THE WORLD."

"I knew that," you say.

"SURE YOU DID," says PAL.

Go to 28.

13

"Make me fly!" you tell PAL.

You turn into a flying fish.

"I meant a bird!"

"WHAT SORT?"

The shark is right behind you. "Never mind ..."

You leap out of the water, but as you glide over the waves, a shadow falls on you from above.

You look up to see a frigate bird diving at you — and they eat flying fish!

Before you can react, the bird opens its beak.

DA-DA-DAAAH!

Out of the frying pan, into the fire.
Go back to 1.

Deep in the bowels of the ship, it is dark and quiet but you find nothing of interest.

To find the captain's cabin, go to 30.
To find the crew's quarters, go to 23.

"Quick, PAL," you whisper, "turn me into a rope!"

Instantly, you find yourself sliding across the deck.

"What have you done now?" you ask.

"DIDN'T YOU WANT TO BE A **SOAP**?"

"No! I said, '**ROPE**'!" But it's too late.

The crewman come along and one of them slips on you. "Hey," she calls, "what fool left soap down here?"

"No idea," says the other. "Chuck it over."

Moments later you splash into the freezing cold water. Before you can change form, you start to dissolve as the boat disappears into the darkness.

You've slipped up! *Go back to 1.*

16

You turn into a giant pair of scissors and snip frantically at the incoming kitchen products. But the cling film wraps round you faster than you can cut it. You turn back into human form. Now you are strong enough to tear the cling film; so **SUSHI MAN** changes his tactics. He waves his arms again, and a roll of seaweed uncoils and wraps itself around you until you look like a giant Swiss roll ...

YOU'VE BEEN SUSHIED! *Go back to 1.*

In a flash you reveal your **MEGAHERO** identity (and pump up your muscles for effect). The old lady escapes.

"Why did you try to rob her?" you ask.

"Don't hurt us, **MEGAHERO**!" squeals one teenager. "*OOOOOH!*"

"It wasn't our fault," moans another. "It was SUSHI MAN — *AAAAAAAH!*"

"He made us do it," sobs the third, clutching at his belly. "He poisoned us — *EEEEEEK!* I need the little boys' room ..."

Desperate for the toilet, they stagger away. You let them go — but you are puzzled. Who is SUSHI MAN?

You need more information — but you are hungry after all that flying and changing.

To find a restaurant, go to 41.

To go to police headquarters, go to 25.

18

Swerving to avoid the net gives the killer whale time to catch up. It lunges at you, jaws open.

DA-DA-DAAAH!

It's called a killer whale for a reason!
Go back to 1.

19

"I want to be a bear!" you tell PAL.

Suddenly you have no clothes on and it's rather cold in the processing plant.

"PAL, I said **'A BEAR'**, as in polar bear, not **'I WANT TO BE BARE'** as in starkers ...!"

"OH, PICKY, PICKY."

You change into a polar bear. The sumo wrestlers attack, but you are much stronger. Then an alarm sounds, and more sumo wrestlers arrive carrying nets. Moments later, you are caught!

You need to change into something that can slip through the net!

To turn into a mouse, go to 46.
To turn into a crab, go to 39.

In rhino form, you charge at the sumo wrestlers and knock them over like bowling pins.

Wasabi Boy laughs. "Nice going, *MEGAZERO*," he gloats. "But see how you like my **WASABIVISION!**"

The criminal stares at you, and his eyes glow green. You immediately find yourself in the grip of a ghastly gut ache, and an outbreak of wind that makes the walls shake.

Wow, you think, *this* **Wasabi Boy** *is hot stuff!*

To turn into a bulldozer, go to 27.

To turn into something that can take away your wind, go to 35.

You head for the biggest **WHOOSHI SUSHI** restaurant in Tokyo. You sneak round the back and into the kitchen, where you change into a cockroach.

You creep about, but don't see anything unusual. Suddenly, a cry goes up. You spin round, and find yourself cornered by a huge angry-looking chef.

Before you can change or dodge, he brings a big cast iron frying pan down on you!

DA-DA-DAAAH!

That didn't pan out well. *Go back to 1.*

Having become a coat, you hang about for a while — until a porter comes along, collects all the coats from the rack and dumps them in a laundry basket. He carrries this into a steaming hot laundry room where he starts dropping the coats into a hot tub. You're about to be boiled alive!

DA-DA-DAAAH!

The heat is on! *Go back to 1.*

23

In the crew's quarters, off-duty fishermen are playing cards, watching a game show or talking about baseball. You can't hear anything useful.

To find the captain's cabin, go to 30.
To get closer so you can hear more, go to 49.

24

PAL turns you into a bluebottle and you buzz off, zigzagging to escape. But **SUSHI MAN** waves his arms, and strips of sticky flypaper shoot from the shelves and wrap themselves around you until you are bound and helpless.

DA-DA-DAAAH!

That's a wrap! Go back to 1.

25

You find the police headquarters. Soon, you are talking to Inspector Nakamura.

"Those teenagers were poisoned by **SUSHI MAN** and his sidekick, *Wasabi Boy*," says Nakamura. "They have developed a toxin from the FUGU. FUGU is eaten as a delicacy, but if it isn't carefully prepared, it can be deadly. **SUSHI MAN**'s poison gives his victims terrible belly ache and wind. Then he orders them to commit crimes for him. If they do, he sends them the antidote in bottles of specially made soy sauce. If they don't then they don't get the antidote."

"Where does the poison come from?" you ask.

"We suspect," says Nakamura, "that it is being distributed through the **WHOOSHI SUSHI** restaurant chain."

Talking of sushi reminds you that you're hungry.

To go to WHOOSHI SUSHI HQ, go to 10.

To go to a WHOOSHI SUSHI restaurant, go to 41.

26

The moment you have changed, the box opens, and you are grabbed and dumped onto a moving belt. Before you can change again, the belt drops you into a flash-freezer. You can't move or speak! The belt moves towards a huge saw used for cutting up frozen fish! *DA-DA-DAAAH!*

You're too chilled! *Go back to 1.*

You turn into a bulldozer and use your blade to scoop up *Wasabi Boy*, along with the sumo wrestlers. You dump the whole lot in a huge vat of sticky hoisin plum sauce!

As they struggle in the gloopy goo, SUSHI MAN appears. "Park right there, *MEGAHERO*," he snarls, "or you'll be wrapped!"

You are puzzled. "What, like in hip-hop?"

"Not RAPPED! WRAPPED, with a 'W'! My superpower is wrapping things. That's why I make such excellent sushi!"

To change into human form, go to 37.

To drive at SUSHI MAN, go to 48.

28

"Turn me into a plane," you tell PAL.

You turn into a paper aeroplane.

"A proper plane!" you say.

You turn into an old-fashioned biplane held together with wire.

You sigh. "Something faster!"

"WHY DIDN'T YOU SAY?" asks PAL.

Seconds later, you have become a military jet fighter, speeding over the sea.

Arriving outside Tokyo, you become a pigeon. As you fly into the city centre, you look down and see an old lady being mugged by three teenagers. They are all clutching their bellies and breaking wind hard enough to blast holes in their undies.

"Give us all your money," one says. "Or we —

OOOOOOH!"

BLAAAAAAAART!

POOOOOOOOOT!

THWRRRRRRP!

How strange! you think. *Mugging is very rare in Japan.*

To turn into something scary, go to 6.

To turn back into *MEGAHERO*, go to 17.

The first thing you remember about pufferfish is that they can blow themselves up to make it difficult for predators to swallow them. You do this.

Unfortunately, the *second* thing you remember is that this doesn't work against tiger sharks.

The shark attacks ...

DA-DA-DAAAH!

You're a shark attack snack! *Go back to 1.*

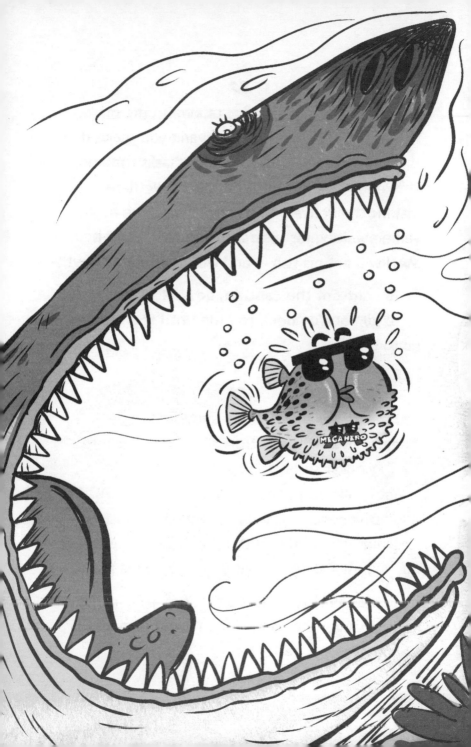

30

The captain is in his cabin, talking to the mate. He has left the door half-open and you go inside.

"You're sure the coast is clear?" asks the mate.

"Relax," the captain tells him. "We'll be making the delivery in a remote bay. The buyer will be waiting for us in a speedboat. **SUSHI MAN** will get his fish — and we'll get our money!"

To confront the captain, go to 45.

To go back on deck to hide until the drop, go to 8.

31

You remember that you are supposed to be finding out how the pufferfish venom gets into Mr Fugumoto's sushi, so you swim into the net.

You realise that any Japanese fisherman who catches a penguin is going to be very surprised. Penguins live in the southern oceans, miles away. So, you ask PAL to change you into a tuna fish.

To stay in fish form, go to 42.

To change into something that can sneak about the ship, go to 2.

32

You turn back into a pufferfish. The crew arrive and start loading the catch into boxes. Soon you are packed in ice along with other fish, and the lid is placed on the box.

After a while, you feel the box moving. Then an outboard engine starts up. You realise the box you are in is being taken ashore.

Eventually the box stops moving — you are on dry land.

To change into an ice cube, go to 11.

To change into a herring gull, go to 40.

33

You scuttle towards the teenagers.

One of them raises his boot.

THERE'S NO TIME TO ACT – you are about to be SQUISHED!

DA-DA-DAAAH!

You've been booted off the case.

Go back to 1.

32–33

PAL turns you into a chimpanzee wearing a leotard.

"**CHAMP**," you say, "not **CHIMP**!"

It's too late! The sumo wrestlers are much bigger and heavier — you are losing by 17 falls and 28 submissions when they go for the knockout ...

DA-DA-DAAAH!

You're no champ, chump! **Go back to 1.**

PAL turns you into a goat.

"Why a goat?" you cry.

"GOATS EAT ALMOST ANYTHING WITHOUT GETTING INDIGESTION, SO WASABI BOY'S **WASABIVISION** WON'T AFFECT YOU!"

PAL is right. Your pain disappears.

You have fun charging round and butting sumo wrestlers where it hurts. But there are too many of them. One grabs you by the horns and holds you helpless in his grip, while *Wasabi Boy* prepares to give you a killer karate chop.

DA-DA-DAAAH!

No ifs or butts — *go back to 1.*

"PAL, turn me into an elephant!" you say.

You turn into a big furry insect.

"What's this?" you ask.

"A **HAIRY ANT**," says PAL.

"I said an **ELEPHANT!**"

"ALL RIGHT, THERE'S NO NEED TO SHOUT!"

As you become an elephant, Mr Fugumoto's bodyguards attack you, but their blows just bounce off your tough skin. You knock two men over with your tusks. Then you wrap your trunk around Mr Fugumoto, and squeeze ...

"WHO IS SUSHI MAN?" you bellow.

"I don't know!" gasps Mr Fugumoto. "I don't work for him and I don't know how his poison gets into my food! When you said you were on official business, I thought you were a food inspector — *OOOOOH!*"

As you release your grip, Mr Fugumoto doubles up in pain. All his bodyguards are holding their bellies and letting off thunderclaps of wind!

Have they really been poisoned, or are they trying to trick you?

If you believe Mr Fugumoto, go to 3.
If you don't, go to 47.

37

You take your human form. "**SUSHI MAN**, I'm here to arrest you."

"Good luck with that!" sneers **SUSHI MAN**.

He raises his hands and rolls of cling film leap from nearby shelves and wrap themselves around you. You are becoming an Egyptian mummy!

To turn into something sharp, go to 16.

To turn into something that can dodge, go to 24.

To become microscopic, go to 5.

38

You decide to find out how **SUSHI MAN** makes his poison by following his supply chain from when the pufferfish are first caught.

You turn into a seagull and fly out over the ocean. Landing on the water near a fishing boat, you transform into a pufferfish.

A shadow approaches. You gulp. It's a tiger shark — and they eat pufferfish!

To stay as a pufferfish, go to 29.

To turn into a something that can fly, go to 13.

To change into something faster than a tiger shark, go to 7.

Turning into a tiny crab, you scuttle through the mesh of the net and hide. It looks to the startled guards as if you've disappeared into thin air.

They head off looking for you before a man in a white coat approaches the steel door and puts his eye to a light. You realise that this is a retina scan, and no disguise will fool it. But you also spot a rack of white coats and a pile of clipboards beside the door.

To disguise yourself as a coat, go to 22.

To disguise yourself as a clipboard, go to 9.

You give PAL the order, and suddenly you have flowers round your neck. You're also wearing a grass skirt and playing a ukulele.

"I said, '**HERRING GULL**'," you yell at PAL, "not **HULA GIRL!**"

"SORRY, IT'S A BAD SIGNAL."

The crew see you and before you can change, one of them cracks you over the head with a frozen cod!

You've had your chips! *Go back to 1.*

You find a **WHOOSHI SUSHI** restaurant. The manager shows you to a table.

The waiter arrives with your sushi and you gobble it up. Then you spot a note that had been hidden underneath your plate.

> *You have been poisoned by the deadly venom of the FUGU pufferfish.*
>
> *Have a nice day,*
>
> *Sushi Man*

You try to get up, but the room, and your legs, have gone all wobbly.

DA-DA-DAAAH!

You should have spotted that the food was fishy! *Go back to 1.*

As you wonder what will happen next, a man in a white hat appears and grabs you by the tail. You realise the terrible truth — this man is the ship's cook, and you're about to be the crew's supper!

Before you can change form, you are lying on a marble slab about to be filleted!

DA-DA-DAAAH!

Don't lie there gasping like a fish out of water! Go back to 1.

43

The box opens and all the fish are taken out. Then the lid is put back, and the box starts to move again.

After a while, the box is opened and you feel yourself falling.

SPLASH!

The used ice cubes — including you — have been dumped in the sea! You start to melt ...

DA-DA-DAAAH!

You're all wet! Go back to 1.

"Turn me into a rabbit!" you tell PAL.

You try to hop it between the legs of the startled heavies. They are too slow to stop you.

But one of them puts his fingers to his lips and gives a piercing whistle. The door bursts open again, and a vicious-looking guard dog appears. Your heart sinks — you can't outrun it. It's time for another change!

Go to 36.

45

You turn back to human form, and point a finger at the astonished captain. "I know all about your evil scheme! You are under arrest!"

You get no further. The mate, who has sneaked round behind you, gives you an expert karate blow that sends you to bye-bye land.

You got the chop! Go back to 1.

46

The surprised guards think you have disappeared as you slip through the net. But you have failed to notice the cats that hang around the factory begging for fish-heads — and looking for mice.

One pounces. You're about to be a kitty treat.

DA-DA-DAAAH!

Look what the cat dragged in! Go back to 1.

47

While Mr Fugumoto and his bodyguards roll around, you phone the police.

"I think Mr Fugumoto is **SUSHI MAN**," you say. "Get here quickly and arrest him."

Thirty minutes later, Inspector Nakamura arrives with a squad of policemen. But just as she is about to arrest Mr Fugumoto her radio squawks out a message:

All units report to First National Bank. Robbery in progress — ten billion yen has been stolen by parping pensioners and guffing girl scouts. Sushi Man and Wasabi Boy have been spotted directing operations ...

"If **SUSHI MAN** is robbing a bank five miles away," snaps the inspector, "he cannot be lying on the floor here, breaking wind! You have wasted police time, *MEGAHERO*. You are no longer welcome in Japan."

OOPS! You've been blown out. *Go back to 1.*

48

You rev your engine and drive at **SUSHI MAN**, who waves his arms. Your caterpillar tracks jump off their rollers and wind themselves around you until you can't move. You change to human form — just in time for **SUSHI MAN** to wrap you in a gigantic sheet of seaweed.

DA-DA-DAAAH!

You've been sushied! *Go back to 1.*

49

Moving along a shelf, you knock over a mug half-full of cold coffee. This drips down the back of one of the crew. He looks up, spots you and gives a startled yell. He makes a dive at you.

You dash into the corridor and run straight into three crew members holding wooden clubs. They see you and pounce ...

DA-DA-DAAAH!

Rats! *Go back to 1.*

SUSHI MAN, *Wasabi Boy* and their gang are soon behind bars and their victims have been given the antidote to the pufferfish poison.

Inspector Nakamura takes you for a slap-up meal to celebrate. Unfortunately, the menu is in Japanese and you can't read it.

"What are we having?" you ask the inspector.

She grins. "FUGU! Japan's most famous delicacy!"

"PUFFERFISH?" You shake your head. "I'll stick to noodles!"

The End!

I HERO

MEGAHERO

THE POISONOUS PLANS OF
PROFESSOR WEIRD

Steve Barlow · Steve Skidmore
Illustrated by Pipi Sposito

EDGE

1

You are in the **MEGA** cave inventing some new **MEGA** gadgets when the **MEGA** alarm sounds ...

"INCOMING **MEGA** MESSAGE," says PAL.

"The world probably needs saving again," you sigh. "Who is it?"

"THE CITY MAYOR ..."

"Put her on ..."

The screen lights up to reveal a very hairy figure!

Hmmm, you think, *that's strange!* You put on your **MEGA** good manners voice. "If you don't mind me saying, Mayor, you seem to be a little bit more hairy than last time we spoke."

"Yes," replies the mayor. "I have a **MEGA** hair problem. I need your help."

If you wish to listen to the mayor, go to 18.

If you want to tell her to see a hairdresser, not a **MEGAHERO**, go to 33.

CONTINUE THE ADVENTURE IN:

THE POISONOUS PLANS OF
PROFESSOR WEIRD

About the 2Steves

"The 2Steves" are
Britain's most popular
writing double act for
young people, specialising
in comedy and adventure.
They perform regularly in
schools and libraries, and at festivals, taking the
power of words and story to audiences of all ages.

Together they have written many books, including the
I HERO Immortals and *iHorror series*.

About the illustrator:
Pipi Sposito

Pipi was born in Buenos Aires in
the fabulous 60's and has always
drawn. As a little child, he used
to make modelling clay figures, too.
At the age of 19 he found out
he could earn a living by drawing. He now develops
cartoons and children's illustrations in different
artistic styles, and also 3D figures, puppets and
caricatures. Pipi always listens to music when he works.

Have you completed these I HERO adventures?

I HERO Immortals — more to enjoy!

Dinosaur Hunter
Steve Barlow – Steve Skidmore
Illustrated by Judit Tondora

978 1 4451 6963 7 pb
978 1 4451 6964 4 ebook

Fairy
Steve Barlow – Steve Skidmore
Illustrated by Judit Tondora

978 1 4451 6969 9 pb
978 1 4451 6971 2 ebook

Knight
Steve Barlow – Steve Skidmore
Illustrated by Judit Tondora

978 1 4451 6957 6 pb
978 1 4451 6959 0 ebook

Pirate Queen
Steve Barlow – Steve Skidmore
Illustrated by Judit Tondora

978 1 4451 6954 5 pb
978 1 4451 6955 2 ebook

Samurai
Steve Barlow – Steve Skidmore
Illustrated by Judit Tondora

978 1 4451 6960 6 pb
978 1 4451 6962 0 ebook

Witch
Steve Barlow – Steve Skidmore
Illustrated by Judit Tondora

978 1 4451 6966 8 pb
978 1 4451 6967 5 ebook

Defeat all the baddies in Toons:

KILLER CUSTARD
Steve Barlow • Steve Skidmore

978 1 4451 5930 0 pb
978 1 4451 5931 7 ebook

ROBIN HAMSTER
Steve Barlow • Steve Skidmore

978 1 4451 5921 8 pb
978 1 4451 5922 5 ebook

ENTER the PENGUIN
Steve Barlow • Steve Skidmore

978 1 4451 5924 9 pb
978 1 4451 5925 6 ebook

KUNG FU KITTEN
Steve Barlow • Steve Skidmore

978 1 4451 5918 8 pb
978 1 4451 5919 5 ebook

Also by the 2Steves...

GALAXY FOOTBALL CUP

978 1 4451 5985 0 hb
978 1 4451 5986 7 pb

MOVIE STAR SET-UP

978 1 4451 5976 8 hb
978 14451 5977 5 pb

ROBOT RAMPAGE

978 1 4451 5982 9 hb
978 1 4451 5983 6 pb

SMALL WORLD

978 1 4451 5972 0 hb
978 1 4451 5971 3 pb

SPACE CHASE

978 1 4451 5892 1 hb
978 1 4451 5891 4 pb

SPACE PIRATES

978 1 4451 5988 1 hb
9781 4451 5989 8 pb

SPACE RAP

978 1 4451 5973 7 hb
978 1 4451 5974 4 pb

WEB WORLD

978 1 4451 5979 9 hb
978 1 4451 5980 5 pb